Empowering My Inner Teen

A Shadow Work Activity Book for Healing Your Inner Teenage Rage

This book is dedicated to you!
You are a beautiful person on a journey of self acceptance and I want you to know that I see you and I accept you!

The companion shadow workbooks:
Embracing My Shadow
Integrating My Shadow
Parenting With My Shadow
are available on Amazon.

For more content from the creator of this journal head to https://linktr.ee/uncensoredintuition

Shadow work is a journey to accept and integrate all the aspects of ourselves that we see as unlovable, unworthy, shameful, etc. Sometimes these are perspectives that are imposed on us in childhood by the people tasked to care for us. However, around adolescence, those perspectives start to seem confusing. We could call this cognitive dissonance; opposing beliefs that our brain cannot determine as true or false. As we are developing and understanding our emotions and thoughts as adults we may question past beliefs and experiences. If not addressed, that questioning inner teenager wants answers. With the activities in this book you are accessing those hidden aspects of yourself with the goal to understand, accept and heal them.

While the inner child represents our core needs and emotions, the inner teenager is the part of your personality responsible for acting on those needs and emotions. When the inner teen is confused, hidden or ignored, negative emotions like anger, sabotage, defiance, manipulation, etc. begin to surface as actions in adulthood.

These are some signs that your inner teenager needs your help: Blaming others, overspending, people-pleasing, controlling behavior, overindulging in activities like eating, substance misuse, promiscuity, etc. These actions are an attempt at feeling relief from the cognitive dissonance where what we know and what we feel are not aligned.

It may also seem like the inner teen is protecting the inner child but teenagers haven't developed appropriate decision-making abilities. What it's really doing is protecting itself from feeling the negative emotions of our inner child and those conflicting beliefs; what was imposed versus what we feel. Suppressing guilt, shame etc from inner child wounds and replacing them with dramatic actions begins to affect our life. The inner teen can act compulsively and impulsively. This can look like self-sabotaging behavior. The goal is to channel those reckless behaviors into healthy ones so you can trust your inner teen.

What your inner teen needs include things like truth, their own identity, acceptance, validation, respect and independence from the parental figure. Currently, that parental figure is you. You are now able to parent (re-parent) your teenage self with the awareness of what your specific needs were and allowing that version of you to release some bottled up emotions.

With the help of this book, *Integrating My Shadow* and the *Embracing My Shadow Workbooks*, you will begin noticing patterns in your behavior that make you ask yourself *Why do I do that?* Understanding why is key to changing the behavior.

Let's begin with channeling some anger!

The important factors here are 1) you are directing it at what you are angry about instead of a loved one or yourself and 2) this will help you clear out the cobwebs so that you can approach this work with more clarity.

Step 1: Fill each box with something you have been holding onto that makes you angry.

Step 2: Turn the page a quarter turn so that it is oriented in landscape direction. Write over and across your anger boxes with everything you want to say to it, all the obscenities in your vocabulary. Gush verbal rage all over them!

Step 3: Write a vow to yourself to take this journey with clarity that is no longer clouded with anger. Any anger that is expressed will be addresses in a healthy manner.

Step 1 going this direction

Step 2 going this direction

I vow to myself _____

Withdraw from withdrawal!

What is your escape habit? Choose something unhealthy that you do to distract yourself from your emotions. It could be shopping, alcohol, hook ups etc.Stop doing that habit for one week. Reflect on your progress here..

Day 1   □ I succeeded   □ I'll succeed tomorrow

How it went:

Day 2   □ I succeeded   □ I'll succeed tomorrow

How it went:

Day 3   □ I succeeded   □ I'll succeed tomorrow

How it went:

Day 4   □ I succeeded   □ I'll succeed tomorrow

How it went:

Day 5   □ I succeeded   □ I'll succeed tomorrow

How it went:

Day 6   □ I succeeded   □ I'll succeed tomorrow

How it went:

Day 7   □ I succeeded   □ I'll try another week

How it went:

From your current self's perspective, what do you need to apologize to your teenage self for?

_____

_____

_____

_____

_____

_____

_____

_____

_____

_____

_____

_____

_____

_____

_____

_____

_____

_____

_____

Activity

Think of a movie or TV show that you weren't allowed to watch. Invite your inner teenager to watch it with you! Even if you have already seen it. Use this space to write a review or draw a character or scene. Use your creativity to channel the teenager inside, they will appreciate this.

Recall an event where someone else's opinion stopped you from doing something.What was the thing you didn't do? Where is the person that prevented you from doing this currently? How would it feel to do the thing now?

_____

_____

_____

_____

_____

_____

_____

_____

_____

_____

_____

_____

_____

_____

_____

_____

_____

_____

_____

_____

_____

_____

_____

_____

Activity

What is something you gave up on in high school that you still think about? Do some research on the subject and use this page to record your findings. These prompts can get you started:

I once gave up on_____

Because_____

_____

Do I regret not pursuing it?_____

Could I pick it back up? _____

What I would need to get started (tools, supplies etc)

_____

_____

_____

_____

_____

_____

_____

Classes/lessons I could take to get started (where/when)

_____

_____

_____

_____

_____

_____

_____

Costs involved:_____

How I would feel if I brought this back into my life

_____

_____

_____

_____

_____

_____

_____

What is something you did as a teen that you regret? How does it affect you now? Apologize to yourself. How will you show yourself forgiveness?

_____

_____

_____

_____

_____

_____

_____

_____

_____

_____

_____

_____

_____

_____

_____

_____

_____

_____

_____

_____

_____

_____

_____

Activity

Recall one thing that made you feel safe as a teen and recreate or incorporate it into your life.

What is the biggest thing you feel you wasted time on in middle or high school? If you could go back and warn yourself would you have listened? What can you do about it now? How will you release this?

Activity

Recall one thing that made you feel <u>loved</u> as a teen and recreate or incorporate it into your life.

How do you handle rejection? When did you first feel rejected as a teen? Who rejected you? How did you react? How would you respond now? How will you soothe your rejected teen self?

_____

_____

_____

_____

_____

_____

_____

_____

_____

_____

_____

_____

_____

_____

_____

_____

_____

_____

_____

_____

_____

_____

_____

_____

Activity

Find an
object
you own that holds
negative memories
or reminds you of
feelings you no
longer welcome in
your life. Destroy
it! (Use safety
measures please)

What is something you do now that brings you joy but you couldn't do as a teen. Who can you share that with?

_____

_____

_____

_____

_____

_____

_____

_____

_____

_____

_____

_____

_____

_____

_____

_____

_____

_____

_____

_____

Activity

Rage cry! Find or create a safe space where you can rage and/or cry. Maybe try one of these:

★ Home alone? Use the shower to scream away things that you want to say but haven't been safe to do so. Watch them wash down the drain.

★ Drive to the middle of nowhere (as close to alone as you can get if you're in a big city) scream into to the wind and hope the sentiment reaches its target.

★ Find a "Rage Room" near you. Some areas have Rage Rooms where you can safely break stuff to release fear, anxiety, trauma, etc for a fee.

★ No physical space to go to? Rage visualize! Find a comfortable position as if you are meditating and visualize whatever physical rage activities you want. Pro tip: the voice in your head can scream as long as it wants since it doesn't have to stop to breathe.

How did it go?

_____

_____

_____

_____

_____

_____

_____

_____

_____

What areas of your life do you crave chaos? When? Have you noticed any specific times or events that spark this need? What can you do about it?

Activity

What article of clothing or accessory did you want as a teenager, but could not have either for financial reasons or parental control? Do you still want it? Using financial responsibility of course, treat yourself! Wear it! If it's not in your current budget or you no longer desire to have it, give yourself the time to reminisce about it!

What were you forced to suppress that surfaces from time to time? Who forced you to suppress it? When does it surface? How can you safely address and embrace it?

Activity

If someone has ever told you that the color you were wearing didn't look good on you, try this! Where that color! Even if it was more like "why do you always wear black? Don't you have anything with color?" Wear the black! You can color this page all black if you want too.

Did you have a friend that wasn't friend material? What did they do? How does it still affect you? How can you forgive yourself for holding onto that?

_____

_____

_____

_____

_____

_____

_____

_____

_____

_____

_____

_____

_____

_____

_____

_____

_____

_____

_____

_____

_____

_____

Activity

Eat something you weren't allowed to eat. Make a whole family meal around it or a dinner party with friends. Celebrate your freedom to eat as you please!

*Unless it was due to an allergy of course

What were you responsible for that shouldn't have been your responsibility? Whose responsibility should it have been? Who is responsible for it now? Is there a pattern to break?

Activity

What dolor did you want to paint your room as a teen? Is there a room you can paint that color now? If you aren't able to paint your home because you rent or live with others, here are some alternatives:

★ Paint or reupholster some furniture
★ Update your bedding to that color
★ Seat covers in your vehicle
★ Use a decor app to digitally "paint" the room and screenshot it
★ Paint on a canvas using that as your main color

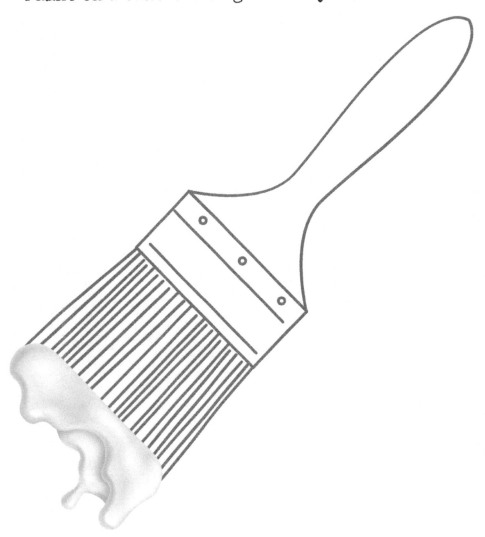

Who is someone that has often made you feel guilty? How and about what? Why should you not feel guilty about this?

Activity

Write a letter to someone from the past who helped you. Thank
them. Give it to them if you can. Use this as a rough draft page.

Activity

Write a letter as your inner teen to an abuser telling them off.
Tear it from the book, read (scream) it aloud and then burn it or
destroy as you wish.

Byee
eeee

What is something you tend to overreact to? Does this feeling remind you of any events in the past? Was there a pattern in the past that you may be repeating? How do you want to react?

Activity

Make a list of things you weren't allowed to say that should have
been acceptable and start saying them.

_____   _____

_____   _____

_____   _____

_____   _____

_____   _____

_____   _____

_____   _____

_____   _____

_____   _____

_____   _____

_____   _____

_____   _____

_____   _____

_____   _____

_____   _____

_____   _____

What do you have to offer in a friendship? What boundaries should you have?

Activity

What non-physical trait are you insecure about? Examples can include: learning capacity, past mistakes, skill confidence, clumsy, etc. Create an affirmation for yourself and repeat it to yourself regularly, put it on a sticky note in your car, on your bathroom mirror, near your work space or somewhere you will see it daily.

I am

_____

_____

If you find yourself looking for a way to distract yourself, what emotion do you feel when it happens? What ways can you find relief that keeps you engaged in what you are avoiding?

_____

_____

_____

_____

_____

_____

_____

_____

_____

_____

_____

_____

_____

_____

_____

_____

_____

_____

_____

_____

_____

_____

Activity

Design a shield for the inner teen to use to protect the inner child. Use tools and symbols specific to to what they are being protected from.

What time period is missing from your childhood memories or is difficult to recall? Do you need to recall it? Why or why not? Do you try to repress feelings now? Is there a correlation?

Activity

Design a shield for the inner teen to use to protect them from the inner child's emotions. Use symbols representing acceptance. The shield is not intended to block the emotions but to accept them as past emotions but not to allow them to take over your current emotions.

What situation or event has occurred in your life that discouraged your creativity? How can/do you motivate yourself to be creative now?

_____

_____

_____

_____

_____

_____

_____

_____

_____

_____

_____

_____

_____

_____

_____

_____

_____

_____

_____

_____

_____

_____

Activity

Use your creativity to create anything you like. Be slightly sloppy (avoid perfectionism) ask someone to critique it. Allow yourself to accept the input as just information without expectations of approval or recognition.

*Do NOT make any changes to your creation.

If the person who is providing feedback seems hesitant, consider the possibility that you may have reacted unfavorably in the past to criticism, particularly if you know this person well. This isn't always the case as the other person may have had a bad experience correcting others in their own past.

What did you create?

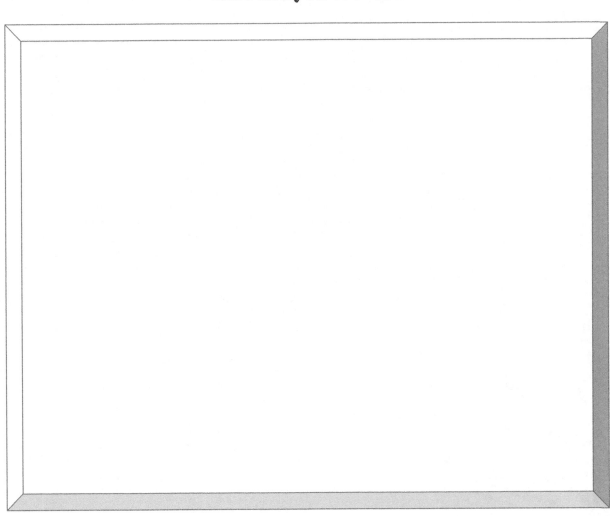

What were you taught about boundaries? How do you react to others boundaries and what expectations do you have for others regarding your own boundaries?

_____

_____

_____

_____

_____

_____

_____

_____

_____

_____

_____

_____

_____

_____

_____

_____

_____

_____

_____

Activity

You pick the music! Create a playlist of songs or music you weren't allowed to listen to as a teen. Listen to it as often as you like!

_____   _____

_____   _____

_____   _____

_____   _____

_____   _____

In what ways do you project your trauma onto others? Do you have specific expectations of people based on past experiences with someone different? How is this destructive?

_____

_____

_____

_____

_____

_____

_____

_____

_____

_____

_____

_____

_____

_____

_____

_____

_____

_____

Activity

Help a stranger in need instead of energy vampires that drain you and don't change. Pretty specific isn't it? When you help someone that truly needs it, and shows genuine appreciation, it can help you to gain clarity on who in your life is draining you simply because you allow it. You allow it by continuing to "help" them. Do they actually need help though? This activity is something that may take several runs to achieve the clarity you are seeking. With regular attempts you should be able to notice the difference between someones sincere gratitude and when someone has already expected you to extend yourself to them. This applies not only to financial help but things like babysitting, picking up after them, loaning items (did you get that back from them yet?) giving rides and generally being available to them without regard for your own time, energy or needs.

Finish this list with things you can do:

Hold the door open

Let them ahead of you in line

Leave an unexpected tip

Recall a time when you purposely avoided responsibility and allowed someone else to take it. Reflect on your own role in that situation. Does your inner teen have some guilt to process here?

_____

_____

_____

_____

_____

_____

_____

_____

_____

_____

_____

_____

_____

_____

_____

_____

_____

_____

Activity

Make a decision without
consulting anyone else!

That's it.
That's the activity.

What is something you have done specifically for recognition that you didn't really want to do?
How often do you do this? Why?

Activity

Inner child visualisation meditation

Set your space (No distractions, incense, soft music or running water, etc)

Connect to your inner teen. Sit or lay in a comfortable position, in a quiet space when you will have plenty of time. You want to make sure you don't need to end your session abruptly.

Once you are in position, you can speak aloud or in your head, state that you would like to speak to your teenage self. You may want to ask permission to speak to them in the beginning sessions, particularly if there are traumas related to boundary violations. Visualize your teenage self, use a photo if it helps, you may ask some questions or listen to what they want to tell you..

Remember that you are speaking to a child. Keep it light at first, ideally let them do all the talking. Listen to them, validate their feelings. Seek to gather information, facts etc. don't analyze them during the communication. Have a conversation, validate and listen. The time for processing is after the conversation ends. Do this exercise as often as possible.

What is something you must have complete control over in your current life? When did you start feeling powerless? How are they connected? How else can you feel empowered?

You have reached the of this journal but not the end of this journey! Shadow work is never done, you will always reach more of yourself!
If you enjoyed this journal, please let me know in your Amazon review and make sure to check the author page for the other books in this series:
Embracing My Shadow
Integrating My Shadow
Parenting With My Shadow

Peace to you on your healing journey!